THE ELEPH___

Stage

D0005609

The world was very different ___ ___ ___. For many
people, life was cold, wet and dark without electricity.
Many people never saw a doctor, and died in misery.

This is the story of a poor, ugly man. Nobody loved
him, everyone laughed at him. They put him in a cage,
like an animal at the zoo. Then one day a doctor saw
him and thought, 'This poor man is interesting. I want
to study him.' Slowly, the Elephant Man became
famous, and everyone wanted to meet him. Even the
Queen visited him!

Why did people first run away from him, then ask to see
him? In this book, you will learn how the Elephant Man
became a 'real' person.

Tim Vicary is an experienced teacher and writer. He
lives and works in York, in the north of England.

OXFORD BOOKWORMS
Series Editor: Tricia Hedge

OXFORD BOOKWORMS

For a full list of titles in all the Oxford Bookworms series,
please refer to the *Oxford English* catalogue.

～ Black Series ～

Titles available include:

～Stage 1 (400 headwords)
*The Elephant Man *Tim Vicary*
*The Monkey's Paw *W.W.Jacobs*
Under the Moon *Rowena Akinyemi*
*The Phantom of the Opera *Jennifer Bassett*

～Stage 2 (700 headwords)
*Sherlock Holmes Short Stories
   Sir Arthur Conan Doyle
*Voodoo Island *Michael Duckworth*
*New Yorkers *O.Henry* (short stories)

～Stage 3 (1000 headwords)
*Skyjack! *Tim Vicary*
Love Story *Erich Segal*
Tooth and Claw *Saki* (short stories)
Wyatt's Hurricane *Desmond Bagley*

～Stage 4 (1400 headwords)
*The Hound of the Baskervilles
   Sir Arthur Conan Doyle
*Three Men in a Boat *Jerome K. Jerome*
The Big Sleep *Raymond Chandler*

～Stage 5 (1800 headwords)
*Ghost Stories *retold by Rosemary Border*
The Dead of Jericho *Colin Dexter*
*Wuthering Heights *Emily Brontë*
I, Robot *Isaac Asimov* (short stories)

～Stage 6 (2500 headwords)
*Tess of the d'Urbervilles *Thomas Hardy*
Cry Freedom *John Briley*
Meteor *John Wyndham* (short stories)
Deadheads *Reginald Hill*

Many other titles available, both classic and modern.
*Cassettes available for these titles.

～ Green Series ～

Adaptations of classic and modern stories for younger readers.
Titles available include:

～Stage 2 (700 headwords)
*Robinson Crusoe *Daniel Defoe*
*Alice's Adventures in Wonderland *Lewis Carroll*
Too Old to Rock and Roll *Jan Mark* (short stories)

～Stage 3 (1000 headwords)
*The Prisoner of Zenda *Anthony Hope*
*The Secret Garden *Frances Hodgson Burnett*
On the Edge *Gillian Cross*

～Stage 4 (1400 headwords)
*Treasure Island *Robert Louis Stevenson*
*Gulliver's Travels *Jonathan Swift*
A Tale of Two Cities *Charles Dickens*
The Silver Sword *Ian Serraillier*

OXFORD BOOKWORMS COLLECTION

Fiction by well-known authors, both classic and modern.
Texts are not abridged or simplified in any way. Titles available include:

From the Cradle to the Grave
   (short stories by *Saki, Evelyn Waugh, Roald Dahl,
   Susan Hill, Somerset Maugham, H. E. Bates,
   Frank Sargeson, Raymond Carver*)

Crime Never Pays
   (short stories by *Agatha Christie,
   Graham Greene, Ruth Rendell, Angela Noel,
   Dorothy L. Sayers, Margery Allingham,
   Sir Arthur Conan Doyle, Patricia Highsmith*)

The
Elephant Man

Tim Vicary

OXFORD UNIVERSITY PRESS

Oxford University Press,
Walton Street, Oxford OX2 6DP

Oxford New York
Athens Auckland Bangkok Bombay
Calcutta Cape Town Dar es Salaam Delhi
Florence Hong Kong Istanbul Karachi
Kuala Lumpur Madras Madrid Melbourne
Mexico City Nairobi Paris Singapore
Taipei Tokyo Toronto
and associated companies in
Berlin Ibadan

OXFORD and OXFORD ENGLISH
are trade marks of Oxford University Press

ISBN 0 19 421640 3

© Oxford University Press 1989

First published 1989
Twelfth impression 1996

No unauthorized photocopying

Illustrated by Nick Harris

Printed in England by Clays Ltd, St Ives plc

Chapter 1

The Creature in the Shop

My name is Dr Frederick Treves. I am a doctor at the London Hospital. One day in 1884, I saw a picture in the window of a shop near the hospital. I stopped in front of the shop and looked at the picture. At first I felt interested, then I felt angry, then afraid. It was a horrible, ugly picture. There was a man in the picture,

One day, Dr Treves saw a picture in a shop near the hospital.

1

but he did not look like you and me. He did not look like a man. He looked like an elephant.

I read the writing under the picture. It said:

Come in and see the Elephant Man. 2 pence.
I opened the door and went in.

There was a man in the shop. He was a dirty man in an old coat with a cigarette in his mouth. 'What do you want?' he asked.

'I'd like to see the elephant man, please,' I said.

The man looked at me angrily. 'Well, you can't,' he said. 'The shop's closing now. You can come back tomorrow.'

'I'm sorry,' I said. 'But I would like to see him now. I have no time tomorrow – I have a lot of work to do. But I can give you more than 2 pence.'

The man looked at me carefully. Then he took the cigarette out of his mouth and smiled with his yellow teeth.

'All right, sir,' he said. 'Give me twelve pence then.'

I gave him the money and he opened a door at the back of the shop. We went into a little room. The room was cold and dark, and there was a horrible smell in it.

A creature sat on a chair behind a table. I say a creature, because it was not a man or a woman, like you or me. The creature did not move or look at us. It sat very quietly on the chair in the cold, dark, dirty

2

room, and looked at the table. The creature had a cloth over its head, because of the cold. On the table in front of it, there was a dead flower.

'Stand up!' said the shopkeeper, loudly.

The creature stood up slowly. It took the old cloth off its head, and put it on the chair.

It sat very quietly on the chair in the cold, dark, dirty room.

I looked at the creature and felt sad. I am a doctor, so I know a lot about accidents and ill people. I see horrible, ugly things every day. But this creature, this thing, was the worst of all. There were no men or women in the hospital like him.

He wore some old trousers, but no shirt, coat, or shoes, so I could see his body very well. His head was the most interesting thing. It was very, very big – like an enormous bag with a lot of books in it. The head did not have much hair, and there was another bag of brown, dirty skin at the back of it. This skin came down below his neck. I could not see one of his eyes very well, because a lot of skin came down in front of his face, too.

An enormous red tooth came out of his mouth, under his nose. It looked like an elephant's tooth. The mouth and nose were like holes in the face. The face could not smile or laugh or look angry or sad, because the skin could not move. It was dead, like an elephant's face.

There were more bags of dirty skin on the front and back of the creature's body. These bags came down to his legs. The right arm was enormous, and there were bags of skin on it, too. The right hand was like a man's foot.

But the left hand – the left arm and the left hand

were beautiful! The left arm had wonderful skin, and the fingers of the left hand were long and beautiful. It was like a young woman's hand!

'Walk, Merrick!' said the shopkeeper angrily. 'Come on, quickly, move!' He hit the creature with his hand.

Slowly, the creature walked across the room. But he could not walk well. His legs were very big and fat, and he had a bad back. He could not walk far without a stick.

'All right, thank you,' I said. 'Let him sit down. I don't want to see any more.' I felt ill, and the smell in the room was very bad.

'Yes, sir,' said the shopkeeper. 'Sit down, Merrick.'

The left hand was like a woman's hand; the fingers were long and beautiful.

We went out of the room and closed the door. The shopkeeper smiled at me with his yellow teeth.

'Wonderful, sir, isn't it?' he said. 'The best Elephant Man in England! Hundreds of people come to see him, you know, hundreds! I take him all over the country, I do!'

'Yes, very interesting,' I said. 'Can I sit down?'

'Yes, sir, of course. Here's a chair.' He looked at me, smiling. 'Would you like a glass of water, sir?'

'Yes, please,' I said. Then I looked at the things in the dirty shop. There were two or three bad apples and some old black bananas: that was all. 'Er, no . . . no, thank you. I'm all right,' I said. 'Did you . . . did you call the creature Merrick?'

'That's right, sir. Joseph Merrick. The best Elephant Man in England! I take him all over the country, you know. Lots of people want to see him.'

'Yes, I see. Do you get a lot of money?'

'Well, sometimes we do, sir, yes. But it's difficult, you see, sir, because of the police. The police don't like us, you see, sir. So we can't stay in a town very long. We usually move every week.'

'Yes, I see. Well, anyway, Mr . . . er?'

'Silcock, sir. Simon Silcock.'

'Yes, well, Mr Silcock, I'm a doctor at the London Hospital. My name is Dr Treves. I think this . . . er . . .

Then I looked at the things in the dirty shop.

this man Joseph Merrick is very interesting, and I would like to see him at the hospital. I want to look at him more carefully, you see.'

'Yes sir, I see. But how can he get to the hospital? It's going to be difficult.'

'Why, man? The hospital's not far from here.'

'Well, yes, sir. I know. But, you see, Merrick can't walk very well. He needs help.'

'You can come with him. Do you want more money? Is that it?'

'Well, yes, sir, I do. But, you see, people are afraid of him too . . . In the road, little boys always run after him

7

and hit him. Then the police get angry because people are afraid. Sometimes they take us to prison.'

'I see,' I said. 'Well, how can he come to the hospital, then?'

'Bring a cab, sir,' said Silcock. 'You can take him to the hospital in a cab.'

Chapter 2

The Card

So next day, at seven o'clock, I came to the shop in a cab. There were not very many people in the road, because it was early in the morning. In November it is dark at seven o'clock in the morning, and I could not see the shop very well. I waited five minutes. A postman walked past. Then the door of the shop opened, and the creature, Merrick, came out.

I could not see his face or his body. He had an enormous black hat on his head, like a big box. A grey cloth came down from the hat, in front of his face. There was a hole in the cloth in front of his eyes. He could see out of the hole but I could not see in. He wore a long black coat, too. The coat began at his neck, and ended at his feet, so I could not see his arms, his body, or his legs. On his feet he wore big shoes, like old bags.

He had a stick in his left hand, and he walked very slowly. I opened the door of the cab, and got out.

'Good morning, Mr Merrick,' I said. 'Can you get in?'

'Elpmyupasteps,' he said.

'I'm sorry,' I said. 'I don't understand.'

For a minute he stood by the door of the cab and said nothing. Then he hit the cab with his stick.

'STEPS!' he said loudly. 'Help me up the steps!'

'Help me up the steps!'

Then I understood. There were three steps up into the cab, and he could not get up them.

'Yes, I see. I'm sorry,' I said. 'Let me help you.'

I took his left hand and began to help him. My right hand was behind his back. I felt very strange. His left hand was like a young woman's, but his back, under the coat, was horrible. I could feel the bags of old skin on his back under the coat.

He put one enormous foot on the first step, and then he stopped. After a minute, he moved his second foot slowly. Then he stopped and waited again.

'Hello, sir. Can I help you?'

I looked behind me. It was the postman. And behind him, I could see three young boys. One of the boys laughed.

The postman smiled. 'Is the gentleman ill?' he asked.

I thought quickly. 'Yes. But this is a lady, not a gentleman. I'm a doctor, and she's ill. Take her hand, so I can help her better.'

The postman took Merrick's left hand, and I helped him with two hands from behind. Slowly, very slowly, Merrick went up the steps and into the cab.

One boy was very near the cab. He called to his friends.

'Come and see this, boys! A fat lady in a black coat! And look at that enormous hat!'

10

The boys laughed. They were very near the cab too, now. I closed the door quickly.

'Thank you,' I said to the postman.

'That's all right, sir,' he said. 'She's a strange lady, sir, isn't she?'

'She's ill, that's all,' I said quickly. 'We're going to the hospital. Goodbye, and thank you.'

The cab drove down the road to the hospital. I looked at Merrick. 'That was difficult, wasn't it?' I said.

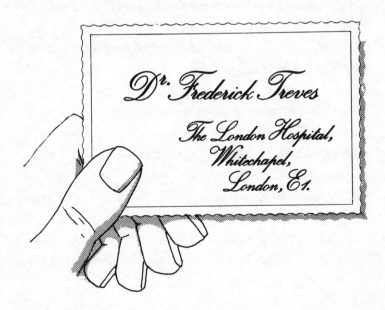

Dr Frederick Treves

The London Hospital,
Whitechapel,
London, E1.

'*Here is my card.*'

11

At first he said nothing, but then he spoke. His voice was very strange, but I listened to him carefully, and I could understand him.

'The steps were very difficult,' he said. 'But most things are difficult for me.'

'Yes,' I said. 'Nothing is easy for you, is it?'

'No,' he said. He was very quiet for a minute. Then he said, 'Who are you, sir?'

'Who am I? Oh, I'm sorry. My name is Dr Treves. Here, this is my card.'

I gave him a card with my name on. Then I thought, 'That was no good. This man can't read.' But Merrick took the card and looked at it very carefully. Then he put it in his trousers pocket.

I did not talk to him very much at the hospital. I looked at his head and arms and legs and body very carefully. Then I wrote the important things about him in a little book. A nurse helped me. Merrick looked at her sometimes, but she did not smile at him or talk to him. I think she was afraid of him. I think Merrick was afraid too, because he was very quiet.

At four o'clock I took him back to the shop in a cab. The next day I looked in the shop window again, but the picture was not there.

Chapter 3

A Letter to 'The Times'

I did not see Merrick again for two years. Then, one *tired* day, the police found him. He had my card in his hand, *hungry* so they brought him to the London Hospital. He was *dirty* very tired, hungry, and dirty, so I put him to bed in a quiet little room. But he could not stay at the hospital. He was not ill, and of course the beds in the hospital are for ill people. We have no beds for hungry people, or ugly people.

One day the police brought Merrick to the hospital.

The Elephant Man

I told the Hospital Chairman, Mr Carr Gomm, about Merrick. He listened carefully, and then he wrote a letter to the editor of The Times newspaper.

From The Times, December 4th, 1886
A Letter to the Editor.

Dear Sir,
  I am writing to you about a man in our hospital. He needs your help. His name is Joseph Merrick, and he is 27 years old. He is not ill, but he cannot go out of the hospital because he is very, very ugly. Nobody likes to look at him, and some people are afraid of him. We call him 'The Elephant Man'.

  Two years ago, Merrick lived in a shop near the London Hospital. For two pence, people could see him and laugh at him. One day Dr Frederick Treves - a hospital doctor - saw Merrick, brought him to this hospital, and looked at him carefully. Dr Treves could not help Merrick, but he gave him his card.

  Then the shopkeeper, Silcock, took Merrick to Belgium. A lot of people in Belgium wanted to see him, and so after a year Merrick had £50. But then Silcock took Merrick's £50, left Merrick in Belgium, and went back to London.

  Merrick came back to London by himself. Everyone on the train and the ship looked at him, and laughed at him. In London, the police

14

put him in prison. But then they saw Dr
Treves's card, and brought Merrick to the
London Hospital.

This man has no money, and he cannot work.
His face and body are very, very ugly, so of
course many people are afraid of him. But he
is a very interesting man. He can read and
write, and he thinks a lot. He is a good,
quiet man. Sometimes he makes things with his
hands and gives them to the nurses, because
they are kind to him.

He remembers his mother, and he has a
picture of her. She was beautiful and kind, he
says. But he never sees her now. She gave him
to Silcock a long time ago.

Can the readers of The Times help us? This
man is not ill, but he needs a home. We can
give him a room at the hospital, but we need
some money. Please write to me at the London
Hospital.

Yours faithfully,

F. C. Carr Gomm

F.C. Carr Gomm.
Chairman of the London Hospital

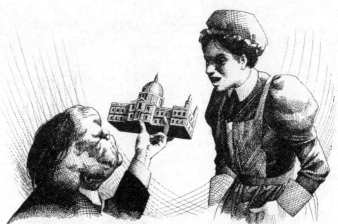

Sometimes he makes things with his hands and gives them to the nurses.

The readers of The Times are very kind people. They gave us a lot of money. After one week, we had £50,000, so Merrick could live in the Hospital for all his life. We could give him a home.

Chapter 4

Merrick's First Home

We gave Merrick two rooms at the back of the hospital. One room was a bathroom, so he could have a bath every day. Soon his skin was much better, and there was no horrible smell.

16

The second room had a bed, table, and chairs. I visited him every day, and talked to him. He loved reading, and talking about books. At first he did not know many books: the Bible, and one or two newspapers, that's all. But I gave him some books of love stories, and he liked them very much. He read them again and again, and talked about them often. For him, the men and women in these books were alive, like you and me. He was very happy.

But sometimes it was difficult for him. At first, one or two people in the hospital laughed at Merrick because he was ugly. Sometimes, they brought their friends to look at him. One day a new nurse came to the hospital, and nobody told her about Merrick. She

We gave Merrick two rooms at the back of the hospital.

17

A new nurse saw Merrick: she screamed and dropped his food on the floor.

took his food to his room, and opened the door. Then she saw him. She screamed, dropped the food on the floor, and ran out of the room.

I was very angry with the nurse, and went to see Merrick. He was not happy about it, but he was not very angry. I think he felt sorry for the girl.

'People don't like looking at me. I know that, Dr Treves,' he said. 'They usually laugh or scream.'

'Well, I don't want nurses to laugh at you, Joseph,' I said angrily. 'I want them to help you.'

'Thank you, doctor,' he said, in his strange slow voice. 'But it's not important. Everyone laughs at me. I understand that.'

I looked at him sadly. In his one good hand, his left hand, he had the little picture of his mother. He looked at the picture for a minute, and then put it by a flower on the table. A tear ran out of his eye and down the skin of his enormous, ugly face.

'Dr Treves,' he said, slowly. 'You and the nurses are very kind, and I'm very happy here. Thank you very much. But . . . I know I can't stay here long, and . . . I would like to live in a lighthouse, after the hospital, please. A lighthouse, or a home for blind people. I think those are the best places for me.'

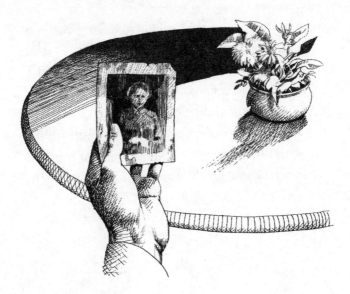

In his one good hand he had the picture of his mother.

19

'What do you mean?' I asked. 'Why?'

He did not look at me. He put the flower on the picture and looked at it carefully.

'Lighthouses have sea all round them, don't they?' he said. 'Nobody could look at me in a lighthouse, so I would be happy there. And blind people can see nothing, so they couldn't see me, could they?'

'But Joseph,' I said. 'This is your home. You live here now. You aren't going to leave the hospital.'

'Not today, perhaps,' he said. 'But soon. You are a kind man, Dr Treves. But I can't stay here very long. I have no money.'

I smiled. 'Joseph,' I said. 'This is your *home* now. Don't you understand? You can stay here all your life.' Very carefully, I told him about the letter to The Times, and the money.

I don't think he understood at first, so I told him again. He was very quiet for a minute. Then he stood up, and walked up and down the room very quickly. A strange sound came from him, like laughing.

A beautiful young woman came to the hospital; she shook Merrick's hand.

Chapter 5

An Important Visitor

I did not want Merrick to live by himself, like a man in a lighthouse. He read his books, and talked to me, but I wanted him to talk to more people. And I wanted him to talk to women.

Merrick read about women in his books, but he did not often talk to women. He met the nurses every day, but they did not talk to him very much. For them, he was always a creature, not a man.

One day, one of my friends, a beautiful young woman, came to the hospital. I told her about Merrick, and took her to his room. She opened the door, and smiled at him.

'Good morning, Mr Merrick,' she said. Then she shook his hand.

Merrick looked at her for a minute with his mouth open. Then he sat down on his bed, with his head in his hand, and cried. He cried for nearly five minutes. The tears ran down his face, between his fingers, and onto the floor.

My friend sat on the bed beside him and put her hand on his arm. She said nothing, but she smiled at

22

For the first time in his life, Merrick had some friends.

him and shook his hand again before she left.

'Dr Treves,' he said to me that night. 'That lady was wonderful! My mother smiled at me once, many years ago, but no women smile at me now. But this lady smiled at me too, and she shook my hand! A beautiful lady smiled at me and shook my hand!'

My young lady friend came again the next week, and talked to Merrick for half an hour. The week after that, she came again with a friend. They gave him some books, and had a cup of tea with him. It was wonderful for him. For the first time in his life, he had some friends. He was a very happy man. He sat in his room, and read his books, and said no more about living on a lighthouse.

23

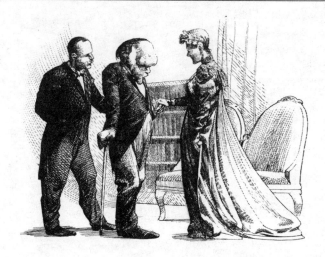

Joseph, this is Her Majesty Queen Alexandra, Queen of England.

People began to read about Merrick in the newspapers, so he had a lot of visitors. Everybody wanted to see him. A lot of important ladies and gentlemen visited him. They smiled at him, shook his hand, and gave him books. Merrick liked talking to these people, and he began to forget about his ugly body. His visitors never laughed at him. He began to feel like a man, not a creature.

One wonderful day, a very important lady came to the hospital to visit him. I met the lady, and took her to his room. Then I opened the door, and smiled at him.

'Good morning, Joseph,' I said. 'There is a new visitor to see you today. A very famous lady.'

24

Merrick stood up beside his table. He did not smile, because his face could not smile, but his eyes looked happy.

'That's good,' he said. 'Who is it?'

I moved away from the door, and the visitor walked in. 'Your Majesty, this is Joseph Merrick,' I said. 'Joseph, this is Her Majesty, Queen Alexandra, the Queen of England.'

Queen Alexandra smiled at him. 'How do you do, Mr Merrick,' she said. 'I'm very pleased to meet you.' Then she shook his hand.

Merrick did not move. For nearly half a minute he stood and looked at her with his mouth open. Then he spoke, in his strange, slow voice.

'How . . . how do you do, Your Majesty,' he said. But I don't think the Queen understood him, because he tried to get down on his knees at the same time. It was very difficult for him, because of his enormous legs.

'No, please, Mr Merrick, do get up,' said the Queen. 'I would like to talk to you. Can we sit at your table?'

'Yes . . . yes, of course,' he said. They sat at the table. She took his left hand, the good hand, in hers. She looked at the hand carefully, and then smiled at Merrick again.

'I often read about you in the newspapers,' she said.

25

'You are a very interesting man, Mr Merrick. You have a very difficult life, but people say you're happy. Is it true? Are you happy now?'

'Oh, yes, Your Majesty, yes!' said Merrick. 'I'm a very happy man! I have a home here now, and friends, and my books. I'm happy every hour of the day!'

'What a wonderful story!' she said. 'I'm very pleased to hear it. Now, tell me about your reading. I see you have a lot of books here.'

'Oh, yes, Your Majesty. I love my books,' said Merrick. And for nearly half an hour they sat and talked about books. The Queen gave him a little book, and some red flowers, before she left.

After her visit, Merrick began to sing. He could not

sing easily, of course, because of his mouth, but all that day there was a strange, happy noise in his room. He looked at the flowers carefully, and put them on his table.

He had many visits from the Queen, and at Christmas she sent him a Christmas card.

> *Windsor Castle*
> *20th December 1888*
>
> *Dear Joseph,*
>
> *Here is a small Christmas present for you. I think it looks like me, doesn't it? I do like visiting you very much, and I am going to come to the hospital again in the New Year.*
>
> *Happy Christmas!*
> *Your friend,*
> *Alexandra.*

The present was a picture of Queen Alexandra, with her name on it. Merrick cried over it, and put it carefully by the bed in his room. Then he sat down and wrote a letter to the Queen. It was the first letter of his life.

The London Hospital
23rd December 1888

My dear Queen,

Thank you very, very, much for your wonderful card and the beautiful picture. It is the best thing in my room, the very best, the most beautiful thing I have. This is the first Christmas in my life, and my first Christmas present. Perhaps I had a Christmas with my mother once, but I do not remember it. I have my mother's picture too, and she is beautiful, like you. But now I know many famous ladies and kind people like Dr Treves, and I am a very happy man. I am happy too because I am going to see you in the New Year.

Happy Christmas to you, my dear friend,

With all my love,
Joseph Merrick

Chapter 6

Outside the Hospital

Merrick had a lot of friends now, but he was more like a child than a man. He could read about things, and talk to his visitors, but he could not go out of the hospital by himself. He thought and played like a child.

After Christmas, he wanted to go to the theatre. This was very difficult, because I did not want the people in the theatre to see him. But a kind lady from the theatre – Mrs Kendal – helped us. We bought tickets for a box at the side of the theatre. We went to the theatre in a cab with dark windows, and we went into the theatre by a door at the back – the Queen's door. Nobody saw us.

Three nurses sat at the front of the box, and Merrick and I sat in the dark behind them. Nobody in the theatre could see us, but we could see the play.

It was a children's Christmas play. Merrick loved it. It was a most wonderful, exciting story. Often he laughed, and sometimes he tried to sing like the children in the theatre. He was like a child. For him, everything in the story was true.

Once he was very afraid, because the bad man in the play was angry and had a knife. At first Merrick

We bought tickets for a box at the side of the theatre.

wanted to leave the theatre, but I stopped him. Then he was very angry with this bad man in the play. He hit his hand on his chair, and stood up and talked to the man. But nobody heard him. When the bad man went to prison, Merrick laughed.

Merrick thought the beautiful young lady in the play was wonderful. He wanted to talk to her too. At the end of the play he was very happy because she married a good young man.

He remembered this play for a long time, and he talked a lot about the people in it. 'What do you think they did after we left?' he asked me. 'Where do the young lady and the young man live? What are they doing now?'

30

'I don't know,' I said. 'Perhaps they live in the country.'

Merrick thought about this for a long time. Then he said: 'Dr Treves, can I go to the country, please? I saw the country once from a train, but I never went there. I often read about it in books. It's very beautiful, isn't it? I would like to see it.'

The visit to the theatre was difficult but a visit to the country was more difficult. But again, one of his new friends helped us. She had a small house in the country, and Merrick could stay in it for the summer, she said.

I took Merrick to the country in a train with dark windows, so nobody could see him. Then we went in a cab to the country house.

There were a lot of trees near the house, but no people lived near it. A countryman brought food to the house every day, but no people came near it.

I stayed with him that night. At night, it was very dark and quiet. In the morning, hundreds of birds sang in the trees, and everything outside the house was green. Merrick walked under the big trees, looking at things happily, and singing his strange song.

I went back to London, but Merrick stayed there for six weeks. He was wonderfully happy. Every week, he wrote me a letter.

31

No people lived near the house in the country.

Apple Tree House,
West Wickham,
Berkshire.
21st July 1889

Dear Dr Treves,

I had a wonderful day again today. It was very warm, so I walked under the trees and sat by a stream.

32

A lot of birds are my friends now.

The water in the stream made a beautiful noise, like singing. Did you know that? I listened to it for two hours.

Lots of little birds came near me. One had a red body in front, and a brown back. I gave it some bread, and it sat on my hand. A lot of birds are my friends, now.

33

I watched the fish in the stream, too. They were very exciting, because they move very fast. One minute they were there, and the next minute I couldn't see them. But I waited quietly, and they always came back. I put my hand in the water, but I couldn't touch them.

I met a big dog yesterday. It made a very loud noise, but I was not afraid. I sat down quietly and looked at it, and it came and smelt my hand. I saw it again today, and gave it some bread. It likes me now.

I am going to put some flowers from the country in this letter. There are hundreds of flowers here. Did you know that? I like the little blue ones best, but they are all beautiful. I have lots of them in my room. I give them water every morning. Little flowers are very thirsty, you know!

I am very happy here, doctor, but I want to see you again soon, too.

> *With love from your friend,*
> *Joseph Merrick*

At the end of the summer he came back to London. He was very well, and his skin looked much better. He talked about the country a lot, but he was happy to see his friends and his books again, too.

Chapter 7

The Last Letter

Six months later, in April 1890, I found him dead in bed. He was on his back in bed, so at first I thought he was asleep. I talked to him, but he did not move. Then I saw that the skin on his face was blue, so I knew he was dead.

He could only sleep with his arms round his legs, and his head on his knees.

heavy
pesado,
inválido

He did not usually sleep on his back. His enormous head was very <u>heavy</u>, so he usually sat up in bed with his arms round his legs, and his head on his knees. He could sleep well like this.

But he wanted to sleep on his back like you and me. He tried to sleep on his back that night, but his heavy head came off the bed, and he broke his neck. He died very quickly.

Next day, the Chairman of the London Hospital, Mr Carr Gomm, wrote to the editor of The Times again.

I found him dead in bed.

36

The Last Letter

The Times, April 16th, 1890

Dear Sir,

Three and a half years ago I wrote to you about a man called Joseph Merrick. This man was called 'The Elephant Man' because he was born with a very ugly body. Merrick was not ill, but he could not work, and he had no money.

The readers of The Times felt sorry for him, and they gave me a lot of money for Merrick. Because of this money, we could give Merrick a home in the London Hospital. It was his first good home, and for three and a half years he lived here happily. The doctors and nurses of the hospital helped him, and many important people visited him. He read many books, he went to the theatre, and in the summer he stayed in the country for six weeks. Because of your readers' money, we could give him a happy life.

Last night Joseph Merrick died quietly in his bed. He was a man with a very ugly body, but he was a good, kind man, and he had a lot of friends. We liked to talk to him, and we are all very sorry because he is dead. A lot of people are going to remember him for a long time.

There is some money left, so I am going to give it to the hospital. Thank you, sir, for your help.

Yours faithfully
F. C. Carr Gomm
Chairman of The London Hospital

Exercises

A Checking your understanding

Chapter 1 *Find answers to these questions in the text.*
1 Where did Doctor Treves work?
2 What did he see in the window of a shop near the hospital?
3 What was the creature's name?
4 Why did the Elephant Man have a stick?

Chapter 2 *Write answers to these questions.*
1 Why were there not many people in the road?
2 Why could Dr Treves not see Merrick's face and body?
3 How did they get to the hospital?
4 What did Dr Treves do to Merrick at the hospital?

Chapters 3 and 4 *Find answers to these questions in the text.*
1 Why did the police bring Merrick to the hospital?
2 Why did Merrick have no money?
3 Who did Merrick have a picture of?
4 What did the nurse do when she saw Merrick?
5 Why did Merrick want to live in a lighthouse?

Chapters 5 and 6 *Are these sentences true (T) or false (F)?*
1 Dr Treves did not want Merrick to talk to women. F
2 Merrick cried because he was unhappy. F
3 Queen Alexandra sent Merrick a Christmas card. T
4 Merrick often went outside the hospital by himself. F
5 One of Merrick's friends had a small house in the country. T

Chapter 7 *How much can you remember?*
1 Where did Merrick die?
2 Did he usually sleep on his back?
3 Did he die quickly?
4 What did Mr Carr Gomm do with Merrick's money?

B Working with language

1 *Complete these sentences with information from the story.*

1 The police brought Merrick to the hospital because . . .
2 Merrick didn't have any money because . . .
3 Merrick's face and body were very ugly so . . .
4 We can give Merrick a room at the hospital but . . .
5 Merrick loved . . .

2 *Put something from A together with something from B to make six true sentences. Check your sentences in chapter 2.*

A	B
1 There were not very many people on the road	7 in his left hand.
2 Treves could not see Merrick's face	8 because she was afraid of him.
3 Merrick had a stick	9 because he had a cloth in front of his face.
4 The postman and Treves	10 in a little book.
5 Treves wrote about Merrick	11 because it was early morning.
6 The nurse did not talk to Merrick	12 helped Merrick into the cab.

C Activities

1 Make a list of things you can find in a hospital.
2 You are a nurse in the hospital. Write a letter to a friend and tell him/her about Joseph Merrick.
3 Because Merrick dies suddenly, the police come to the hospital to see Dr Treves. What questions do they ask Dr Treves about Merrick? What does Dr Treves answer?

Glossary

bath you sit in a bath when you want to wash all your body
began past tense of 'to begin'
below under
beside next to
Bible the most important book for Christians
birds birds have two legs and two wings; usually, they can fly (see the picture on page 33)
box 1) a thing to put other things in: you buy shoes in a shoe box; 2) when you sit in a box in a theatre, only the people in your box can see you (see the picture on page 30)
bread people in most countries eat bread every day: you use bread to make sandwiches
broke past tense of 'to break'
brought past tense of 'to bring'
cab an old word for 'taxi' (see the picture on page 9)
came past tense of 'to come'
card 1) a piece of paper with your name and address on it (see the picture on page 11); 2) you give Christmas cards to your family and friends (see the picture on page 26)
chairman an important man in the hospital
cloth trousers and coats are made from cloth
could past tense of 'can'
country (the) not the town
creature a living animal
did past tense of 'to do'
drop (*v*) to let something fall (see the picture on page 18)
drove past tense of 'to drive'
editor the most important person in a newspaper office
elephant a very big grey animal with a long nose and big ears
end finish
enormous very big
faithfully (see 'yours')
felt past tense of 'to feel'

fingers you have ten fingers: five on your left hand and five on your right hand (see the picture on page 5)

fish fish live in rivers and in the sea

food what you eat

found the past tense of 'to find'

gave past tense of 'to give'

gentleman a man from an important family

glass (*n*) you drink tea from a cup; you drink water from a glass

got past tense of 'to get'

had past tense of 'to have'

hair most people have hair on their heads (see the picture on 43)

heavy it is difficult to carry heavy things: 1,000 kilos is very heavy

himself (by himself) nobody was with him

hip your legs meet your body at your hips (see the picture on page 43)

hit past tense of 'to hit'

hole the cloth has a hole in it, to let Merrick see where he is going

horrible not nice; people are often afraid of 'horrible' things

kind nice, good; a kind person often helps people

knees your knees are between the top of your legs and your feet (see the picture on page 43)

knew past tense of 'to know'

lady a woman from an important family

life your life stops when you die

lighthouse a lighthouse is a tall building with a light on the top: it helps ships in dangerous places

like (*prep*) not different: a river is like the sea, because it is made of water

loudly with a lot of noise

made past tense of 'to make'

Majesty (Her/His/Your) when you speak to a queen or a king, you say 'Your Majesty'

marry when a man and a woman marry, they become husband and wife

met past tense of 'to meet'

mirror you can see your face in a mirror

neck your neck is between your head and your body (see the picture on page 43)

newspaper you read a newspaper to know what is happening in the world

nose your nose is between your eyes and your mouth (see the picture on page 43)

ones 'the little blue ones' means 'the little blue flowers'

place where something or someone is: in a room, a house, a town, etc.

play (*n*) you go to the theatre to see a play

police the police help people; they also put bad people in prison (see the picture on page 13)

present a present is something you give to your friends or your family

put past tense of 'to put'

prison the police put bad people in prison

Queen (the) the most important woman in Britain (see the picture on page 24)

ran past tense of 'to run'

read/rɛd/ past tense of 'to read' /riːd/

sad not happy

said past tense of 'to say'

sat past tense of 'to sit'

saw past tense of 'to see'

scream (*v*) to make a lot of noise because you are afraid or angry

sent past tense of 'to send'

shake (hands) people shake hands when they meet (see the picture on page 21)

shook past tense of.'to shake'

shopkeeper a person who has a small shop

side not the front or the back of a cab (see the picture on page 9)

skin (*n*) you have skin all over your body; some people have white skin, others have yellow, brown or black skin

smell (*n*) flowers have a nice smell; fish have a horrible smell

smell (*v*) you need your eyes to see; you need your nose to smell

smelt past tense of 'to smell'

speak to talk

spoke past tense of 'to speak'

steps place to put your foot when you walk upstairs or downstairs (see the picture on page 9)

stick (*n*) a long piece of wood; Merrick walks with a stick

stood past tense of 'to stand'

strange different

stream a small river
tear (*v*) /tɛə/ to break paper
tear (*n*) /tɪə/ water from your eyes when you cry
theatre where you go to see a play (see the picture on page 30)
thought past tense of 'to think'
told past tense of 'to tell'
took past tense of 'to take'
touch (*v*) to feel something with your hands
ugly not beautiful
understood past tense of 'to understand'
voice you talk with your voice
was/were past tense of 'to be'
went past tense of 'to go'
were (see 'was')
wore past tense of 'to wear'
wrote past tense of 'to write'
Yours faithfully you write this at the end of a formal letter (see page 15)

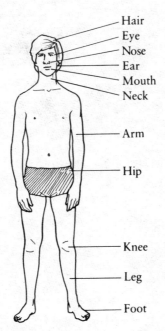